This is Your Life, Charlie Brown!

Selected Cartoons From

IT'S A DOG'S LIFE, CHARLIE BROWN

Vol. I

A FAWCETT CREST BOOK
FAWCETT PUBLICATIONS, INC., GREENWICH, CONN.
MEMBER OF AMERICAN BOOK PUBLISHERS COUNCIL, INC.

Other Peanuts Books in Fawcett Crest Editions:

D1147 YOU'RE MY HERO, CHARLIE BROWN!
D1097 WHO DO YOU THINK YOU ARE, CHARLIE BROWN?
D1070 GOOD OL' SNOOPY
D1134 YOU ARE TOO MUCH, CHARLIE BROWN
D1142 VERY FUNNY, CHARLIE BROWN
D1141 FOR THE LOVE OF PEANUTS!
D1140 WHAT NEXT, CHARLIE BROWN?
D1133 FUN WITH PEANUTS
D1130 YOU'RE A WINNER, CHARLIE BROWN!
D1129 GOOD GRIEF, CHARLIE BROWN!
D1128 HEY, PEANUTS!
D1115 THE WONDERFUL WORLD OF PEANUTS
D1113 HERE COMES CHARLIE BROWN!
D1105 WE'RE ON YOUR SIDE, CHARLIE BROWN
D1099 HERE COMES SNOOPY
D1096 LET'S FACE IT, CHARLIE BROWN

Only 50¢ Each—Wherever Paperbacks Are Sold

If your dealer is sold out, send only cover price plus 10¢ each for postage and handling to Crest Books, Fawcett Publications, Inc., Greenwich, Connecticut 06830. Please order by number and title. If five or more books are ordered, no postage or handling charge is necessary. No Canadian orders. Catalog available on request.

This book, prepared especially for Fawcett Publications, Inc., comprises the first half of *It's a Dog's Life, Charlie Brown,* and is reprinted by arrangement with Holt, Rinehart and Winston, Inc.

First Fawcett Crest Printing, August 1968

Published by Fawcett World Library
67 West 44th Street, New York, N.Y. 10036
Printed in the United States of America

I'M SORRY, SNOOPY, BUT YOU'RE GOING TO HAVE TO SLEEP OUTSIDE...
WE'RE NOT ACCEPTING ANY APPLICATIONS FOR HOUSE-DOG!
RATS!
I THOUGHT THERE MIGHT BE AN OPENING...

ARE YOU INTERESTED IN PEDIATRICS, CHARLIE BROWN?
LISTEN TO THIS..."SOME NEWBORN INFANTS ARE HIGHLY INFECTIOUS TO OTHERS, AND BECAUSE THEY ARE LITERALLY SURROUNDED BY CLOUDS OF BACTERIA, THEY ARE CALLED 'CLOUD BABIES.'"
WELL, WHAT ARE YOU LOOKING AT ME FOR?

I'LL HAVE TO GO BACK TO THE HOUSE...I FORGOT MY RUBBERS...
IN FACT, I FORGOT MY RUBBERS, MY MITTENS AND MY CAP...
SOMETIMES YOUR STUPIDITY AMAZES ME!
I'LL ADMIT THAT IT DOES HAVE A QUALITY ALL ITS OWN!

NOBODY LIKES ME...I DON'T HAVE A SINGLE FRIEND IN THE WHOLE WORLD!
SO I'M ON MY WAY TO THE BARBERSHOP...
SO?
I CAN'T PLAY BASEBALL, I CAN'T PLAY FOOTBALL, I CAN'T PLAY CHECKERS, I CAN'T DO ANYTHING! I'M A COMPLETE FLOP!
I'M GOING TO DROWN MY SORROWS IN A HAIRCUT!

UNBREAKABLE PLASTIC...VERY NEAT....

MY BIG SISTER HIT ME AGAIN
DOES SHE HIT YOU OFTEN?
"OFTEN" ISN'T THE WORD...
SHE IS BEGINNING TO HIT ME WITH ALARMING FREQUENCY!

DO THEY ALWAYS BRING THE COWS IN FROM THE PASTURE AT NIGHT?
OF COURSE, YOU BLOCKHEAD! IF THEY LEAVE THEM OUT OVER-NIGHT, THEY GET PASTEURIZED!!
I NEVER REALIZED THAT.
I GUESS I'D MAKE A LOUSY FARMER!

YOU THINK YOU'RE ALWAYS RIGHT, DON'T YOU?!
WELL, YOU'RE **NOT**! DO YOU HEAR ME? **YOU'RE NOT**!!
THIS IS ONE TIME WHEN I'M RIGHT AND YOU'RE WRONG! I DON'T CARE IF YOU **CAN** ARGUE BETTER THAN I CAN!
YOU JUST SOUND RIGHT!

EXERCISE, THAT'S WHAT WE NEED!
EVERYONE SHOULD START THE DAY WITH THIRTY PUSH-UPS!
HE'S RIGHT...
BUT HOW CAN YOU DO PUSH-UPS WHEN YOUR NOSE GETS IN THE WAY?

ALL YOU EVER THINK OF IS THIS STUPID PIANO!
I SUPPOSE YOU THINK YOU'RE GOING TO BE ANOTHER BEETHOVEN!
I'M GOING TO BE MORE THAN THAT...
I'M GOING TO BE THE SAM SNEAD OF MUSIC!!!

THIS IS THE BEGINNING OF A NEW YEAR, RIGHT? RIGHT!
NOW, LISTEN CAREFULLY... I HAVE A SUGGESTION....
BAD HABITS ARE BEST DESTROYED AT THE BEGINNING OF A NEW YEAR, RIGHT? RIGHT! THAT STUPID BLANKET YOU'RE HOLDING IS A BAD HABIT, RIGHT? RIGHT!
SUDDENLY I FEEL VERY COLD...

THIS IS IT!
WELL, THAT'S THAT! A JOB WELL DONE!
???
I BURIED YOUR BLANKET!

YOU BURIED MY BLANKET?
YOU CAN'T DO THAT! I'LL DIE WITHOUT THAT BLANKET! I'LL BE LIKE A FISH OUT OF WATER! I'LL DIE! I'LL DIE!
TELL ME WHERE YOU BURIED IT! TELL ME!
TELL ME! TELL ME! TELL ME! TELL ME! OH, TELL ME!

SHE WHAT?!
SHE BURIED MY BLANKET, CHARLIE BROWN!
SHE SAID SHE WAS GOING TO CURE ME OF THE HABIT ONCE AND FOR ALL SO SHE BURIED MY BLANKET!
HOW IN THE WORLD AM I EVER GOING TO FIND IT?
NOW I KNOW WHAT THEY MEAN WHEN THEY SAY OUR FUTURE LIES IN THE SOIL!

LINUS TELLS ME YOU'VE BURIED HIS BLANKET.
ARE YOU SURE THAT WAS THE RIGHT THING TO DO?
OF COURSE, IM SURE! I'M **ALWAYS** SURE OF **EVERYTHING** I DO!
WHERE ARE **YOU** GOING?
LINUS ASKED ME TO SIT UP WITH HIM TONIGHT.
THIS FIRST NIGHT WITHOUT THE BLANKET IS GOING TO BE THE HARDEST!

THIS IS GOING TO BE A LONG NIGHT...
IT'S HARD ON A LITTLE KID WHO HAS ALWAYS DEPENDED ON A BLANKET SUDDENLY TO BE DEPRIVED OF IT...
HE'S FEVERISH!

IS IT MORNING YET?
NO, IT'S ONLY TEN O'CLOCK.
TEN O'CLOCK?! GOOD GRIEF! THIS NIGHT IS GOING TO LAST FOREVER! I'LL NEVER MAKE IT! WHY DID LUCY HAVE TO BURY MY BLANKET? WHY?
ANYWAY, CHARLIE BROWN, IT'S NICE OF YOU TO SIT UP WITH ME THIS FIRST NIGHT.
THIS IS WHAT FRIENDS ARE FOR...
GOOD OL' CHARLIE BROWN!

HE'S FINALLY GONE TO SLEEP...
MAYBE IF HE CAN MAKE IT THROUGH THE NIGHT WITHOUT HIS BLANKET, HE'LL BE ALL RIGHT.
SLEEP IS WHAT HE NEEDS... IF HE CAN JUST SLEEP FOR...
WELL, HOW'S HE DOING?!

I'VE GOTTA FIND WHERE LUCY BURIED MY BLANKET!
I CAN'T GO THROUGH ANOTHER NIGHT LIKE LAST NIGHT AGAIN! OH, THE DREAMS I HAD!
WOW!
THAT'S THE FIRST TIME IN MY LIFE I EVER DREAMED ABOUT HYANNIS PORT!

YOU THINK I'M BEING MEAN TO LINUS BECAUSE I BURIED HIS BLANKET, DON'T YOU?
WELL, I'M NOT! I'M REALLY DOING HIM A FAVOR! HE'S TOO WEAK EVER TO BREAK THE HABIT BY HIMSELF! HE'S AS WEAK AS... AS...WHY, HE'S AS WEAK AS YOU ARE, CHARLIE BROWN!
THAT'S A DISTURBING COMPARISON!

I HAVE A SUGGESTION, LINUS...
WHY DON'T YOU LET ME TRY TO FIND SOME SORT OF SUBSTITUTE FOR YOUR BLANKET?
MAYBE I COULD GET YOU A DISHTOWEL OR SOMETHING...
WOULD YOU GIVE A STARVING DOG A RUBBER BONE?

YOU THINK I'M BEATEN, DON'T YOU?
WELL, I'M NOT! I'M GONNA FIND THAT BLANKET IF I HAVE TO DIG UP THE WHOLE NEIGHBORHOOD!
I'LL FIND IT! DO YOU HEAR ME? I'LL FIND IT! I'LL FIND IT!!!
PLEASE TELL ME WHERE IT IS!

EVER SINCE LUCY BURIED MY BLANKET I'VE FELT SORT OF DIZZY...
I CAN'T EVEN EAT...... EVERYTHING TASTES SOUR....
I DON'T SEEM TO BE ABLE TO CATCH MY BREATH EITHER...I FEEL LIKE I'M CHOKING...
PLEASE TELL ME WHERE YOU BURIED IT!

I'VE GOTTA FIND THAT BLANKET, CHARLIE BROWN!
LUCY WON'T TELL ME WHERE SHE BURIED IT SO I'VE GOTTA DIG 'TIL I FIND IT!
I'VE JUST GOTTA DIG AN' DIG AN' DIG UNTIL I FIND IT!
GOOD LUCK!

GOTTA FIND IT! GOTTA FIND IT!
?
GOTTA DIG EVERYWHERE UNTIL I FIND THAT BLANKET! GOTTA FIND IT! GOTTA FIND IT!
GOTTA DIG EVERYWHERE!
GOTTA FIND IT! GOTTA FIND IT!

MY BLANKET!
OH, SNOOPY! YOU FOUND IT!! YOU FOUND IT! YOU FOUND IT! YOU FOUND IT! YOU FOUND IT!
EVERY NOW AND THEN I FEEL THAT MY EXISTENCE IS JUSTIFIED!

I HEAR LINUS GOT HIS BLANKET BACK...
YEAH, THAT NOSY DOG FOUND IT, AND DUG IT UP...OH, WELL, I DON'T CARE ANY MORE...
FROM NOW ON I'M THROUGH TRYING TO HELP PEOPLE.... THEY NEVER APPRECIATE IT ANYWAY...
STUPID DOG!
HEE HEE HEE HEE HEE HEE

MY BLANKET! I GOT IT BACK! I CAN'T BELIEVE IT! MY GOOD OL' BLANKET!
FOR TWO WEEKS IT'S BEEN BURIED BENEATH THE GROUND.
IT'S DIRTY, IT'S RAGGED, IT'S TORN...IT'S EVEN A LITTLE MOLDY...
BUT IT'S MY BLANKET!
SIGH

NO!NO!NO! THAT'S NOT RIGHT!
K A
IF YOU'RE GOING TO LEARN TO COUNT, SALLY, YOU'RE GOING TO HAVE TO PAY ATTENTION...
HERE'S A PICTURE WITH SOME BOATS IN IT...NOW, TELL ME HOW MANY BOATS YOU SEE...
ALL OF THEM!

THE PEOPLE OF THIS WORLD HAVE GONE MAD!
I'M GOING TO STAND ON MY HEAD AS A PUBLIC PROTEST!
I WILL BECOME SYMBOLIC OF THE "LITTLE MAN" CRYING OUT IN ANGUISH AGAINST THE WORLD'S MADNESS...
SNIF? SNIF?
?
...AFTER SUPPER..

!
THERE'S ONLY ONE THING WRONG WITH THIS...
THE RAIN KEEPS RUNNING DOWN MY NOSE INTO MY EYES!

HERE'S A NICE PEBBLE, LINUS... TAKE IT HOME, AND OBSERVE IT.
THE FASCINATING THING ABOUT PEBBLES IS THEIR GROWTH, FOR SOME GROW UP TO BE STONES WHILE OTHERS GROW UP TO BE ROCKS...
YOU SHALL HOPE, OF COURSE, THAT IT GROWS UP TO BE A ROCK, FOR A PEBBLE THAT GROWS UP TO BE A STONE IS LIKE A YOUTH WHO HAS GONE ASTRAY!
SIGH I HAVE SO MUCH TO LEARN!

"SOMETIMES HE WOULD STARTLE PEOPLE IN PUBLIC PLACES."
"HE FLEW OUT IN ANGER AGAINST ALL THAT WAS PETTY, DULL OR GREEDY IN MEN."
"...OFTEN, HOWEVER, HIS SCORN WOULD TURN TO HIGH HILARITY AND HUMOROUS JESTS."
ARE YOU READING ABOUT BEETHOVEN OR MORT SAHL?

THE SUBJECT IS CLOSED, CHARLIE BROWN!
IT SIMPLY GOES WITHOUT SAYING THAT YOU ARE AN INFERIOR HUMAN BEING!
IF IT GOES WITHOUT SAYING, WHY DID YOU HAVE TO SAY IT?

VIOLET, DO YOU REALLY THINK THAT CHARLIE BROWN IS AS HOPELESS AS YOU MAKE HIM OUT TO BE?
HE'S WORSE! HE HAS **NO** REDEEMING FEATURES WHATSOEVER!
I JUST CAN'T THINK OF ENOUGH BAD THINGS TO SAY ABOUT HIM!
I'M INFINITE!

MOM ALWAYS PUTS A NOTE IN MY LUNCH.
HMMM...
"A SMILE EACH DAY WILL BRING HAPPINESS YOUR WAY"
THAT'S NOT A LUNCH...IT'S A CHINESE FORTUNE COOKIE!

Z
BEAGLES ON THE GRASS, ALAS!
I AIN'T NO STUPID BEAGLE!

SEE THAT BUILDING THERE? THAT'S THE LIBRARY.
IF YOU EVER WANT TO BORROW A BOOK, ALL YOU HAVE TO DO IS GO IN THERE AND TELL THEM WHICH ONE YOU WANT, AND THEY'LL LET YOU TAKE IT HOME!
FREE?
ABSOLUTELY FREE!
SORT OF MAKES YOU WONDER WHAT THEY'RE UP TO!

DRAWING WITH CHALK ON THE SIDEWALK IS LOTS OF FUN!
IT'S REALLY A WONDERFUL MEDIUM...YOU CAN GET SOME VERY NICE EFFECTS...
I THINK IT RANKS RIGHT ALONGSIDE TEMPERA AND OIL AS AN ARTISTIC MEDIUM.
OF COURSE, IT HAS ITS DRAWBACKS, TOO

LOOK AT IT THIS WAY, CHARLIE BROWN...
THESE ARE YOUR BITTER DAYS. THESE ARE YOUR DAYS OF HARDSHIP AND STRUGGLE...
BUT IF YOU'LL JUST HOLD YOUR HEAD UP HIGH, AND KEEP ON FIGHTING, SOMEDAY YOU'LL **TRIUMPH**!
GEE, DO YOU REALLY THINK SO, LUCY?
FRANKLY, NO!

THERE WERE TWO NEW BABIES BORN IN OUR BLOCK LAST WEEK
IT'S ALL PART OF THE POPULATION EXPLOSION
REALLY?
I NEVER HEARD A THING!

WHAT ARE YOU GOING TO GET ME FOR BEETHOVEN'S BIRTHDAY, SCHROEDER?
A MILLION-DOLLAR DIAMOND NECKLACE!
THAT WILL BE NICE
I LOVE GEMS!

?
CHARLIE BROWN, I WOULD LIKE VERY MUCH TO HAVE YOU MEET FRIEDA!
HOW DO YOU DO, FRIEDA.
HOW DO YOU DO, CHARLIE BROWN... I HAVE NATURALLY CURLY HAIR!
DO YOU FEEL THAT SPRING WILL BE HERE SOON? I BELONG TO TWELVE RECORD CLUBS! NOW THAT WE'RE GETTING A GOOD PICTURE ON OUR TV, THE PROGRAMS ARE LOUSY!
FRIEDA PRIDES HERSELF ON BEING A GOOD CONVERSATIONALIST!

IT'S RATHER FRIGHTENING TO SEE THE DAYS GO BY SO FAST..
TO SAY THAT GRASS IS GREEN, YOU KNOW, IS NOT SAYING NEARLY ENOUGH...ACTUALLY, I'M VERY GRATEFUL FOR HAVING NATURALLY CURLY HAIR...I REALLY AM...
SOMETIMES MY DADDY CALLS ME "LADYBUG."...I USED TO READ A LOT, BUT LATELY I JUST DON'T SEEM TO HAVE TIME...
FRIEDA SITS BEHIND ME IN SCHOOL...I HAVEN'T HEARD A WORD OUR TEACHER HAS SAID THIS WHOLE SEMESTER!

FRIEDA, THIS IS MY SISTER, LUCY...
HOW DO YOU DO, LUCY? HAVE YOU EVER MET ANYONE BEFORE WHO HAS NATURALLY CURLY HAIR? ACTUALLY, I'M VERY GRATEFUL FOR IT!
SHE'S KIND OF A FRIEND OF MINE, LUCY, AND SHE SITS BEHIND ME AT SCHOOL....
PLEASE DON'T SLUG HER...

YOU'RE THE ONLY ONE AROUND HERE I DON'T UNDERSTAND...
ALL YOU EVER DO IS LIE ON TOP OF THAT DOGHOUSE... YOU SHOULD BE CHASING RABBITS!
YOU GOT IT WRONG, KID...ALL WRONG...
CHASING RABBITS IS "OUT"....LYING ON TOP OF DOGHOUSES IS "IN"!

DON'T FEEL BAD. AFTER ALL, EVERYONE GETS DEPRESSED NOW AND THEN.
PERHAPS YOU SHOULD TRY TO **CHART** YOUR PERIODS OF DEPRESSION, CHARLIE BROWN.
NOW, HOW LONG WOULD YOU SAY **THIS** PERIOD OF DEPRESSION HAS LASTED?
SIX YEARS!

ONLY 78 MORE DAYS UNTIL BEETHOVEN'S BIRTHDAY!
THE OLDER YOU GET, THE FASTER TIME SEEMS TO GO BY!

THAT'S REALLY KIND OF DISILLUSIONING
WHAT'S THE MATTER?
SNOOPY ISN'T AS SMART AS I THOUGHT HE WAS...
HE MOVES HIS LIPS WHEN HE READS!

DID YOU FILL OUT THAT PAPER FOR THE SCHOOL OFFICE?
I HAVE IT RIGHT HERE...
MY MOTHER'S NAME, MY FATHER'S NAME, OUR ADDRESS AND OUR TELEPHONE NUMBER...
WHAT DID YOU PUT DOWN UNDER "FAMILY PHYSICIAN"?
WELL, I WASN'T SURE SO I PUT DOWN "DR. SEUSS"!

WOULD YOU CARE TO HEAR THE LETTER I GOT FROM MY PEN-PAL?
WELL, AS LONG AS I'M STANDING HERE, I MIGHT AS WELL LISTEN.
"DEAR CHARLES BROWN....I THANK YOU FOR YOUR LATEST LETTER...IT WAS SO INTERESTING THAT I READ IT ALOUD TO OUR CLASS AT SCHOOL..."
"WE ALL AGREED THAT YOU MUST BE A VERY NICE PERSON, AND SOMEONE WHO IS PLEASANT TO KNOW."
HA!

"DENTISTS MOSTLY AGREE THAT THUMBSUCKING CAN AFFECT THE SHAPE OF THE TEETH AND JAW...HOWEVER...
...DENTISTS FURTHER AGREE THAT PSYCHOLOGICAL IMPLICATIONS INVOLVED IN PREVENTATIVE STEPS TO CORRECT THE HABIT OF THUMBSUCKING FAR OUTWEIGH THE ORAL PROBLEMS."
DENTISTS ARE A REMARKABLY UNDERSTANDING LOT!

I AM ALWAYS IMPRESSED BY THE CONSTANCY OF THE STARS.

IT GIVES ME A FEELING OF SECURITY TO LOOK UP, AND KNOW THAT THE STAR I SEE WILL ALWAYS BE THERE, AND WILL...

THIS IS THE TIME OF YEAR WHEN I HAVE TO WORK THE HARDEST...
GETTING MY BASEBALL TEAM ORGANIZED IS A REAL JOB... THERE ARE A MILLION THINGS THAT HAVE TO BE DONE..
I HAVE TO NOTIFY ALL THE PLAYERS..I HAVE TO GATHER UP ALL THE EQUIPMENT..I EVEN HAVE TO SEE IF THE INFIELD NEEDS...
...MOWING!

WELL, CHARLIE BROWN, HERE I AM READY TO START A NEW SEASON!
I'M VERY OPTIMISTIC ABOUT OUR CHANCES THIS YEAR, AND FULL OF ENTHUSIASM!!
BY THE WAY, ARE YOU GOING TO BE OUR MANAGER AGAIN?
YES, I GUESS I AM..
I'M VERY PESSIMISTIC ABOUT OUR CHANCES THIS YEAR, AND SUDDENLY I'VE LOST ALL MY ENTHUSIASM!

I THOUGHT YOU SAID YOU WERE GONNA HIT 'EM TO ME?!!

I'LL BE ON YOUR TEAM, CHARLIE BROWN, IF YOU WON'T MAKE ME WEAR A CAP..
I DON'T LIKE TO WEAR A CAP BECAUSE IT COVERS UP MY HAIR...I HAVE NATURALLY CURLY HAIR, YOU KNOW
I DON'T SUPPOSE YOU'VE EVER HAD A PLAYER ON YOUR TEAM WHO HAS HAD NATURALLY CURLY HAIR, HAVE YOU, CHARLIE BROWN?

NO, BUT I'VE HAD MY SHARE OF OTHER PECULIAR KINDS!

I'M GLAD YOU'LL BE PLAYING SECOND BASE FOR US THIS YEAR, LINUS..
I'M ALSO GLAD TO SEE YOU HAVEN'T DRAGGED YOUR BLANKET OUT HERE WITH YOU...AFTER ALL, SECOND BASE IS NO PLACE FOR A BLANKET, IS IT?
MY BLANKET IS SECOND BASE!!

WHOP!
A GOOD MANAGER LEARNS TO MAKE THE BEST USE OF WHATEVER MATERIAL HE HAS!

DO YOU THINK ANYONE WILL BE WATCHING OUR GAMES, CHARLIE BROWN?
WELL, I IMAGINE WE'LL HAVE A FEW SPECTATORS, FRIEDA.
I'LL BE OUT IN CENTER FIELD, WON'T I?
HOW FAR OUT WOULD YOU SAY CENTER FIELD IS?
OH, ABOUT A HUNDRED YARDS...WHY?
FROM THAT DISTANCE DO YOU THINK PEOPLE WILL BE ABLE TO TELL THAT I HAVE NATURALLY CURLY HAIR?

ALL RIGHT, TEAM. LET'S PAY ATTENTION NOW!
WE HAVE A LONG HARD SEASON AHEAD OF US! I'M NOT OFFERING YOU AN EASY TASK! I'M GOING TO ASK FOR SACRIFICE, HARD WORK AND DEDICATION!
I'M GOING TO ASK THAT YOU DRIVE YOURSELVES TO THE VERY LIMITS OF ENDURANCE!
PLEASE?

IT'S NOT FAIR FOR YOU TO ASK US TO SACRIFICE, WORK HARD AND BE DEDICATED!
WE JUST WANT TO WIN BALL GAMES...WE DON'T WANT TO SUFFER!
ALL YOU LEADERS ARE ALIKE!! YOU'RE ALWAYS TRYING TO STIR US UP! WHY DON'T YOU JUST LEAD US, AND STOP BOTHERING US?
YES, WHAT ARE YOU TRYING TO DO, MAKE US NERVOUS ?!

IF YOU'RE GOING TO PLAY LEFT FIELD, VIOLET, YOU'D BETTER PUT ON YOUR GLOVE..
I CAN'T! I'M AFRAID THERE MIGHT BE A SPIDER OR A BUG IN IT!
EVERY DAY I'M AFRAID TO PUT MY GLOVE ON BECAUSE I THINK THAT A BUG MIGHT HAVE CRAWLED INTO IT DURING THE NIGHT!
OH, GOOD GRIEF! HERE, LOOK...I'LL PUT MY HAND IN FIRST...OKAY?
WHEW OKAY.... THANK YOU, CHARLIE BROWN..
IN ALL THE HISTORY OF BASEBALL THERE HAS NEVER BEEN A MANAGER WHO HAS HAD TO GO THROUGH WHAT I HAVE TO GO THROUGH!

HEY, MANAGER, WE'RE AFRAID TO PUT OUR HANDS IN OUR GLOVES BECAUSE THERE MIGHT BE A SPIDER OR A BUG IN THERE!
OH, GOOD GRIEF! HOW DO THESE THINGS EVER GET STARTED?! HERE...LET ME PUT MY HAND IN FIRST JUST TO SHOW YOU THAT.
AAUGH!!
A BUG!
THANK YOU, MANAGER!

MONDAY IS OUR FIRST GAME, AND I FEEL LIKE LEAVING THE COUNTRY!
I'M JUST NOT CUT OUT TO BE A MANAGER, I GUESS...... MY SHOULDERS AREN'T BROAD ENOUGH.
YOU MEAN YOU'RE NOT READY TO ASSUME THE "MANTLE OF RESPONSIBILITY"?
BEFORE IT WILL FIT ME, THE "MANTLE OF RESPONSIBILITY" WILL NEED CONSIDERABLE ALTERATION!

FORTY-EIGHT, FORTY-NINE, FIFTY! HERE I COME, READY OR NOT!

RATS! I DON'T KNOW WHY I EVER PLAY THIS GAME!

DO YOU ALWAYS DRAG THAT BLANKET AROUND BEHIND YOU, LINUS?
AS A MATTER OF FACT, I DO! I SUPPOSE YOU'RE GONNA START IN ON ME NOW!!
NO, I THINK IT'S A GOOD IDEA...I MEAN, IF IT MAKES YOU FEEL MORE SECURE, THEN YOU SHOULD CARRY IT WITH YOU!
SMACK
I HAVE NATURALLY CURLY HAIR.

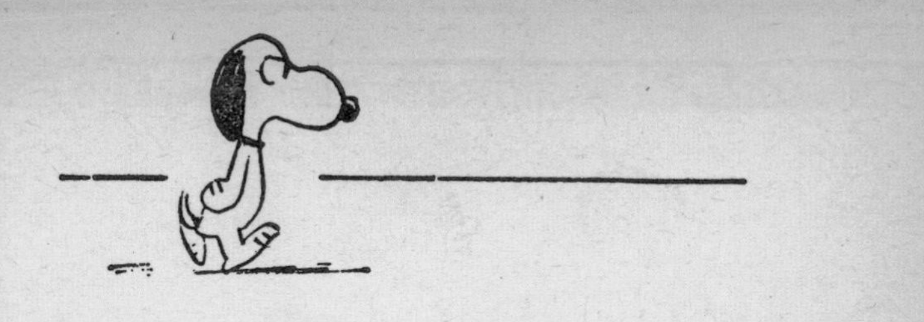

RATS! I'LL BET SHE WOULD HAVE BEEN SCARED IF I HAD **REALLY** BEEN DRACULA!

I WORRY ABOUT YOU, CHARLIE BROWN.
YES, I CAN IMAGINE!
NO, I REALLY DO.
HAVE YOU HAD A PHYSICAL CHECK-UP LATELY?
I THINK YOUR FOREHEAD IS GETTING FAT!

WELL, IT'S TIME TO GO TO SCHOOL.
HAVE A GOOD DAY!
THANK YOU!
BECOME EDUCATED!

WELL, LOOK HERE! A BIG YELLOW BUTTERFLY!
IT'S UNUSUAL TO SEE ONE THIS TIME OF YEAR UNLESS, OF COURSE, HE FLEW UP FROM BRAZIL... I'LL BET THAT'S IT!
THEY DO THAT SOMETIMES, YOU KNOW... THEY FLY UP FROM BRAZIL, AND THEY...
THIS IS NO BUTTERFLY... THIS IS A POTATO CHIP!
WELL, I'LL BE! SO IT IS! I WONDER HOW A POTATO CHIP GOT ALL THE WAY UP HERE FROM BRAZIL?

NO!! ABSOLUTELY NOT!
NO!
OH, ALL RIGHT! GOOD GRIEF!
THIS IS THE ONLY THING I HATE ABOUT CORN-ON-THE-COB!

I GUESS I WON'T BE SEEING YOU UNTIL MONDAY, CHARLIE BROWN...
...SO HAVE A HAPPY WEEK-END.
THANK YOU!
INCIDENTALLY, WHAT **IS** HAPPINESS?

YOU CAN'T DRIFT ALONG FOREVER...
YOU HAVE TO DIRECT YOUR THINKING... FOR INSTANCE, YOU HAVE TO DECIDE WHETHER YOU'RE GOING TO BE A LIBERAL OR A CONSERVATIVE...
YOU HAVE TO TAKE SOME SORT OF STAND... YOU HAVE TO ASSOCIATE YOURSELF WITH SOME SORT OF CAUSE...
ARE THERE ANY OPENINGS IN THE LUNATIC FRINGE?

HOW CAN A PERSON JUST **DECIDE** WHAT HE'S GOING TO THINK?
DOESN'T HE HAVE TO THINK **FIRST**, AND THEN TRY TO DISCOVER WHAT IT IS THAT HE'S **THOUGHT** ?
YOU'RE LOOKING AT ME WITH BLANK EYES!

I DON'T UNDERSTAND WHAT YOU'RE SO WORRIED ABOUT...
WHY SHOULD YOU CARE IF I HAVE ANY OPINIONS OR PERSONALITY OR CHARACTER?
BECAUSE IF YOU DON'T HAVE ANY CHARACTER, IT'S A REFLECTION ON ME!
AH, HA!!

I ALWAYS THOUGHT THAT OPINIONS SHOULD HAVE QUALITY AND NOT JUST QUANTITY.
THAT'S BECAUSE YOU DON'T KNOW ANYTHING ABOUT OPINIONATION!
OPINIONATION?

GET ON YOUR MARK, GET SET....
GO!!
HOW'S THAT FOR SPEED?
?
HE'S BACK ALREADY!

I KNOW SOMETHING YOU COULD GET ME FOR BEETHOVEN'S BIRTHDAY...
YOU COULD GET ME SOME PERFUME!
THAT'S A GOOD IDEA. I'LL GET YOU A BOTTLE OF "EAU DE JUMPROPE"!
I WONDER WHAT IT IS THAT MAKES MUSICIANS SO SARCASTIC!?

MY DAD WAS TELLING ME ABOUT A GOOD PARTY GAME...
YOU SET A MILK BOTTLE ON THE FLOOR BESIDE A CHAIR, AND THEN YOU KNEEL ON THE CHAIR, AND TRY TO DROP CLOTHESPINS INTO THE BOTTLE...
DOESN'T THAT SOUND LIKE IT MIGHT BE A GOOD GAME?
UH HUH.
WHAT ARE CLOTHESPINS?

SOONER OR LATER, CHARLIE BROWN, THERE'S ONE THING YOU'RE GOING TO HAVE TO LEARN...
YOU REAP WHAT YOU SOW! YOU GET OUT OF LIFE EXACTLY WHAT YOU PUT INTO IT! NO MORE AND NO LESS!!
I'D KIND OF LIKE TO SEE A LITTLE MORE MARGIN FOR ERROR!

WHOEVER INVENTED PORTABLE TELEVISIONS NEVER HAD AN OLDER SISTER!

DEAR PENCIL PAL,
WE HAVE A NEW GIRL IN OUR NEIGHBORHOOD. HER NAME IS FRIEDA, AND SHE HAS
NATURALLY CURLY HAIR
NATURALLY CURLY HAIR
THAT'S NOT WHAT I MEANT TO SAY!!!

LOOK! IT'S CHARLIE BROWN'S LITTLE SISTER!
AND SHE'S **WALKING**!
SHE'S WALKING! SHE'S WALKING! SHE'S WALKING!
ISN'T HE THE CUTEST THING?

LUCY'S LOOKING FOR ME, SALLY.
BUT DON'T TELL HER WHICH WAY I WENT, OKAY?
THANK YOU!
SIGH
I'D DO ANYTHING FOR THAT MAN!

THAT UP THERE IS THE SKY, SALLY...
THE SKY HAS CLOUDS, AND STARS, AND WIND AND RAIN... THE SKY IS USUALLY BLUE...
THIS DOWN HERE IS GRASS... GRASS IS USUALLY GREEN...
ISN'T HE WONDERFUL? HE KNOWS EVERYTHING!

YOU SEE, SALLY, ALTHOUGH GRASS IS GREEN, THERE ARE VARIOUS SHADES OF GREEN...
TO SOME PEOPLE THE GRASS IS ALWAYS GREENER ON THE OTHER SIDE OF THE FENCE!
HA HA HA HA HA
HA HA HA HA HA HA
HE EVEN HAS A SENSE OF HUMOR!

WHAT'S GOING ON HERE?
RATS!

LOOK, CHARLIE BROWN, I DON'T SEE WHY YOU SHOULD BE MAD AT ME...
I HAVE NO INTEREST IN YOUR SISTER! AFTER ALL, I'M ALMOST FIVE YEARS OLDER THAN SHE! FIVE YEARS!
FIVE YEARS DOESN'T SEEM LIKE MUCH NOW, BUT IT WILL WHEN WE'RE OLDER...
WHY, GOOD GRIEF, WHEN I'M NINETY-FIVE SHE'LL ONLY BE NINETY!

I THINK IT IS ONLY NATURAL FOR LITTLE GIRLS TO LIKE LITTLE BOYS...
I DON'T THINK ANYONE WOULD DENY THIS... STILL....
EACH OF US HAS MANY YEARS AHEAD OF HIM, AND EACH OF US WILL MEET MANY DIFFERENT PEOPLE..
AFTER ALL, WE ARE STILL CHILDREN, AND WE...
GOOD GRIEF!

YOU'VE GOT THIS ALL WRONG, CHARLIE BROWN.
I CAN'T HELP IT IF YOUR LITTLE SISTER FOLLOWS ME AROUND! WHAT DO YOU WANT ME TO DO, TELL HER TO GO AWAY?!
I DON'T WANT HER HANGING AROUND ME! I DON'T EVEN LIKE LITTLE GIRLS!
SIGH

BLAH!
WHAA

DO YOU EVER PRAY, LUCY?
THAT'S KIND OF A PERSONAL QUESTION, ISN'T IT? ARE YOU TRYING TO START AN ARGUMENT?
I SUPPOSE YOU THINK YOU'RE SOMEBODY PRETTY SMART, DON'T YOU? I SUPPOSE YOU THINK...
YOU'RE RIGHT...RELIGION IS A VERY TOUCHY SUBJECT!

THEY'RE HAVING A GOOD TIME UP THERE ON THAT STAR TONIGHT.
IT LOOKS LIKE THEY'RE REALLY LIVING IT UP.
WHAT MAKES YOU THINK THAT?
THEY'VE GOT ALL THE LIGHTS ON!

SECURITY!! HMMPH!
IF YOU ONLY KNEW HOW STUPID YOU LOOK STANDING THERE HOLDING THAT BLANKET!
BUT I SUPPOSE YOU DON'T CARE HOW STUPID YOU LOOK AS LONG AS YOU'RE SECURE..
THAT'S RIGHT... I'M SECURE IN MY STUPIDITY!

HAVE YOU EVER THOUGHT OF ENTERING SNOOPY IN A DOG SHOW?
I WOULDN'T KNOW WHAT CATEGORY TO PUT HIM IN...I DON'T EVEN KNOW HIS BREED...
HOW ABOUT MISCELLANEOUS?

STOP HIM! STOP HIM! SOMEBODY PLEASE STOP HIM!
OKAY, LINUS... HOLD IT RIGHT THERE!
HERE HE IS, LUCY... ALL SAFE AND SOUND...
?
WHAT I REALLY MEANT WAS TO STOP HIM BEFORE HE DESTROYED HIMSELF INTELLECTUALLY!

DEAR PENCIL-PAL,
IT HAS BEEN A LONG TIME SINCE I LAST WROTE TO YOU.
I WOULD HAVE WRITTEN BEFORE, BUT I FORGOT ALL ABOUT YOU.
SOMEHOW THAT DOESN'T SOUND RIGHT...

DON'T BE ALARMED, CHARLIE BROWN, BUT THERE'S A DINOSAUR COMING!
A WHAT?
A DINOSAUR! A SMALL DINOSAUR!
CLOMP
CLOMP
CLOMP
CLOMP
CLOMP
OH, GOOD GRIEF!
CLOMP
CLOMP
CLOMP

HERE COMES THE BIG DINOSAUR, KING OF THE WORLD!
HERE COMES THE BIG DINOSAUR, KING OF THE WORLD!

ROWR
I'M A LOUSY DINOSAUR!

WHERE DID YOU GET THE NICKEL, FRIEDA?
I GOT IT FROM THE "TOOTH FAIRY." I PUT MY TOOTH UNDER MY PILLOW LAST NIGHT, AND SHE LEFT ME A NICKEL!
ONCE I GOT A DIME, AND ONCE I EVEN GOT A QUARTER!!
DO YOU THINK IT'S TRUE THAT THE PRICES ARE ESTABLISHED BY THE AMERICAN DENTAL SOCIETY?

YEARS AGO PEOPLE USED TO SHOOT OFF FIRECRACKERS ON THE FOURTH OF JULY...
THEY'D LIGHT THESE GREAT BIG "CANNON CRACKERS," SEE, AND...
BOOM!
YEAH, AND ALL THE DOGS ENDED UP UNDER THE BED FOR THE REST OF THE DAY!

DO YOU SEE THIS PICTURE OF THE LITTLE GIRL PLAYING ON THE SOUTH LAWN OF THE WHITE HOUSE?
UH HUH... THAT'S A VERY NICE PICTURE.
DO YOU NOTICE ANYTHING IN PARTICULAR?
OR RATHER, SHOULD I SAY, DO YOU NOTICE THE ABSENCE OF ANYTHING IN PARTICULAR?
NO, WHAT IS IT?
SHE'S NOT HOLDING A BLANKET!!
OH, GOOD GRIEF!

LET ME SEE THAT PICTURE AGAIN OF THE LITTLE GIRL PLAYING ON THE SOUTH LAWN OF THE WHITE HOUSE.
YOU'RE RIGHT...SHE'S NOT HOLDING A BLANKET.
OF COURSE, THERE COULD BE A REASON...
MAYBE HER FOLKS CAN'T AFFORD TO BUY HER ONE!

I'M WRITING A LETTER TO THAT LITTLE GIRL WHO PLAYS ON THE LAWN AT THE WHITE HOUSE...
I'M GOING TO OFFER TO SEND HER A BLANKET IF SHE THINKS SHE'D LIKE ONE...
DO YOU KNOW WHAT HER LAST NAME IS?

I THINK IT IS POSSIBLE TO BE TOO NICE!
BY GOLLY, NOBODY'S GONNA WALK ALL OVER ME! NO SIR! IF ANYBODY'S GONNA DO ANY WALKING, IT'S GONNA BE ME!
THERE'S ONLY ONE WAY TO SURVIVE THESE DAYS...YOU HAVE TO WALK OVER THEM BEFORE THEY WALK OVER YOU!
IT MUST BE NICE TO HAVE A PHILOSOPHY THAT WILL SUSTAIN YOU IN TIMES OF NEED!

WHY SHOULD I GIVE YOU SOMETHING FOR BEETHOVEN'S BIRTHDAY? I DON'T EVEN LIKE YOU!
WELL, I DON'T LIKE YOU EITHER!!
I DON'T EVEN KNOW WHAT'S GOING ON...

I ALWAYS LIKE TO STOP ON MY WAY TO SCHOOL, AND CHECK TO SEE WHAT MOM PUT IN MY LUNCH...
A CHEESE SANDWICH, A BAG OF POTATO CHIPS, AN ORANGE, A CUP CAKE AND A NOTE...
"STUDY HARD, AND SOMEDAY YOU MAY GET TO BE PRESIDENT."
I'M THE ONLY PERSON I KNOW WHO GETS A LUNCH WITH A COMMERCIAL IN IT!

PSYCHIATRIC HELP 5¢
5¢
I'VE BEEN VERY NERVOUS LATELY...
EVERYTHING SEEMS TO UPSET ME. I'M NERVOUS ALL THE TIME...
LEARN TO RELAX.... FIVE CENTS, PLEASE!

YOU'RE SO SMUG!
YOU THINK YOU'VE GOT IT MADE, DON'T YOU? YOU THINK YOU'RE KING BECAUSE YOU'RE THE ONLY ANIMAL AROUND HERE!
WELL, YOU KNOW WHAT I'M GONNA DO? I'M GONNA GET A CAT!
YOU WOULDN'T!?!

A CAT?
SURE, WHY NOT?
I ASKED MY MOTHER IF SHE'D BUY ME ONE, AND SHE SAID SHE WOULD!
BUT WHAT ABOUT SNOOPY? WHAT WILL HE DO WHEN HE HEARS ABOUT THIS?
HE KNOWS ALL ABOUT IT!

A CAT? WHAT IN THE WORLD DO YOU WANT A CAT FOR?
TO PUT SNOOPY IN HIS PLACE! TO SHOW HIM THAT HE'S NOT SO IMPORTANT!
SOMEBODY'S GOT TO TAKE HIM DOWN A FEW NOTCHES!
PLEASE DON'T BOTHER...I'M NOT WORTH IT!

WHAT'S THE SENSE IN GETTING A CAT? WHY STIR UP A LOT OF TROUBLE?
BECAUSE IT HAS TO BE DONE! SNOOPY HAS HAD IT TOO GOOD AROUND HERE FOR TOO LONG A TIME! HE HAS TO BE STOPPED!
SOMEBODY HAS TO PUT HIM IN HIS PLACE!
ARE YOU BRINGING IN A CAT OR A GUNFIGHTER?
TOUCHÉ!!

A CAT! A CAT!
SHE SAID SHE WAS GOING TO GET A CAT!
A CAT! A CAT! A CAT! A CAT! THIS IS DRIVING ME CRAZY! I'VE GOT TO TRY TO PUT IT OUT OF MY MIND!
IT CAN'T BE DONE! IT'S LIKE TRYING TO FORGET THE H-BOMB!
SCHULZ

MAYBE I'M GETTING ALL WORKED UP OVER NOTHING...
MAYBE FRIEDA WILL GET A CUTE LITTLE KITTEN...AFTER ALL, KITTENS ARE A LOT OF FUN..
HA! WHY TRY TO FOOL MYSELF? IT WON'T BE A KITTEN....
IT'LL BE A BLAH CAT!

HEY! COME, AND SEE!
FRIEDA'S GOT HER CAT!!
OH, NO!
IT'S HAPPENING, AND I CAN'T BELIEVE IT!
THIS IS TERRIBLE...
TO ME, CATS ARE THE CRAB GRASS IN THE LAWN OF LIFE!

FRIEDA AND HER CAT..
I CAN HEAR THEM COMING... I CAN'T STAND IT...

THIS IS A CAT ?!!

FARON, THIS IS SNOOPY... SNOOPY, THIS IS FARON.
I'LL LEAVE YOU TWO ALONE TO GET ACQUAINTED...

WHAT DO YOU **SAY** TO CATS?

IT SAYS HERE THAT THE HAWAIIAN WORD FOR "STOMACH" IS "OPU"...
THAT'S VERY INTERESTING..
YOU KNOW, I THOUGHT I WAS GETTING FAT, BUT I GUESS I'M NOT... IN FACT, I THINK I LOOK PRETTY GOOD...
OPUWISE, THAT IS!

LOOK, LUCY, WHY SHOULD ANYONE GIVE ANYONE ELSE A PRESENT ON BEETHOVEN'S BIRTHDAY?
WHY NOT KEEP IT SIMPLE? YOU HAVE A FEW FRIENDS OVER, HAVE A PIECE OF CAKE AND LISTEN TO THE NINTH SYMPHONY...
THAT'S A WONDERFUL WAY TO CELEBRATE BEETHOVEN'S BIRTHDAY!
ALL I WANTED WAS A PRESENT. WHAT DO I GET? A LECTURE ON HOW TO GIVE PARTIES!

NOBODY'S GOING TO GIVE ME ANYTHING FOR BEETHOVEN'S BIRTHDAY
I'M DISILLUSIONED!
YOU KNOW, IT IS KIND OF HARD TO IMAGINE A HOLIDAY WITHOUT A LITTLE GREED ATTACHED TO IT!